GOLD'N OLD'UN's

Published in the UK by
POWERFRESH Limited
Unit 3 Everdon Park
Heartlands Industrial Estate
Daventry
NN11 8YJ

Telephone 01327 871 777
Facsimile 01327 879 222
E Mail   info@powerfresh.co.uk

Copyright © 2006 The Silvey & Jex Partnership
Cover and interior layout by Powerfresh

ISBN   1904967507

Printed in Malta by Gutenberg Press limited

More Jokey Geriatrics from Silvey-Jex

IT SAYS HERE "YOU GET SMALLER AS YOU GET OLDER"
IT CAN'T GET MUCH SMALLER CAN IT?
SJ.

THE YOUNG MAN IN THE GARAGE SLID UNDERNEATH, HE GREASED THE NIPPLES- LUBRICATED EVERYTHING-SO IT'S NOT STIFF ANY MORE
I LOVE IT WHEN YOU TALK DIRTY
SJ.

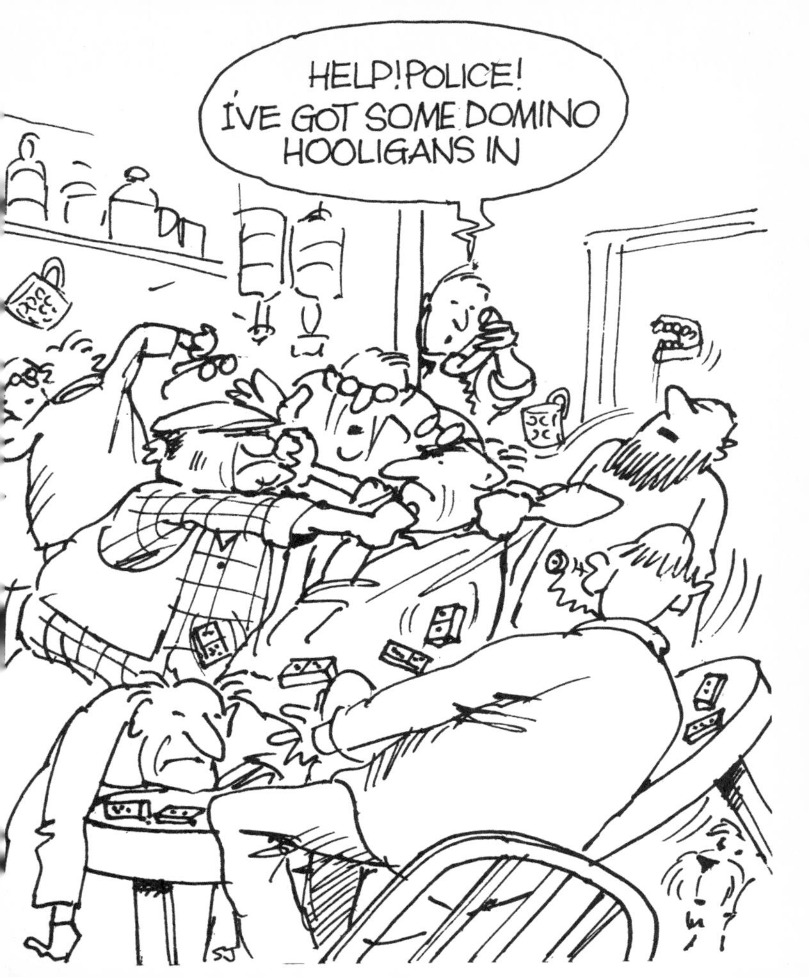
HELP! POLICE!
I'VE GOT SOME DOMINO
HOOLIGANS IN

I'M GOING TO DO A NEW 'CALENDAR GIRLS'. WHICH MONTH DO YOU WANT TO BE?

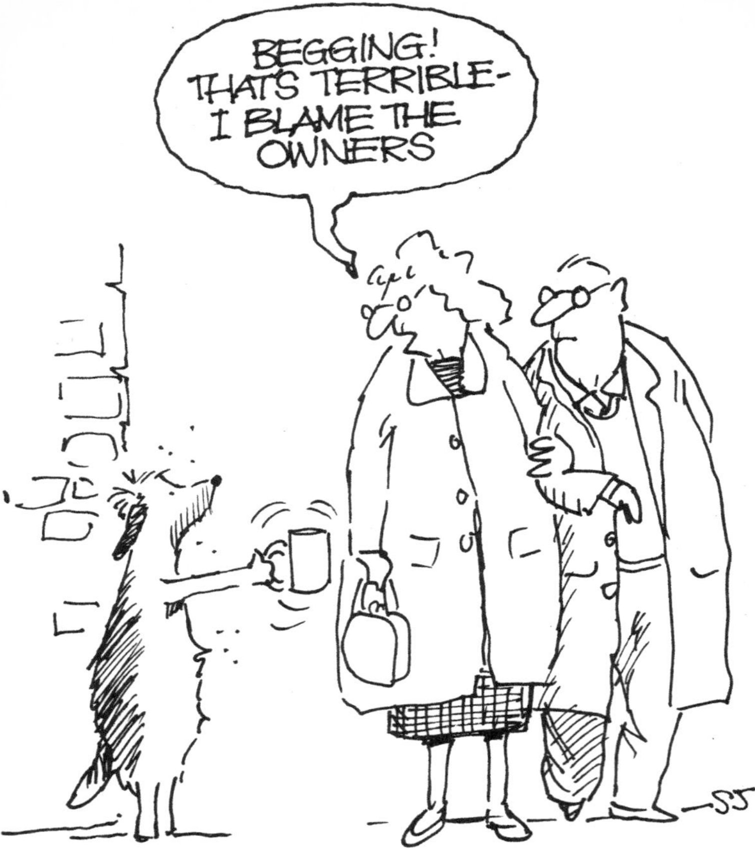
BEGGING! THAT'S TERRIBLE- I BLAME THE OWNERS
SJ

IT'S NOT WHAT YOU THINK
OH SORRY SO I DON'T THINK YOU'RE IN BED WITH A LARGE OCTOPUS?
ST.

I THINK MY FRANK'S GOT HIMSELF A MISTRESS
WELL PERHAPS YOU SHOULD GET YOURSELF A HEADMASTER
J.T.

AND WHO'S BEEN SLEEPING IN MY BED, AND WHO'S GOING TO GET A SMACKED BOTTOM WHEN I FIND OUT
SJ

WE NEVER GO ANYWHERE THESE DAYS
WHY DO YOU THINK THAT IS THEN?
SJ

THEY BETTER BE GOOD...I DON'T WANT YOU SPENDING YOUR POCKETMONEY ON RUBBISH
SJ.

IF YOU DIDN'T MAKE SUCH A FUSS OF THAT CAT YOU'D HAVE SOME DECENT CLOTHES TO WALK AROUND IN
SJ.

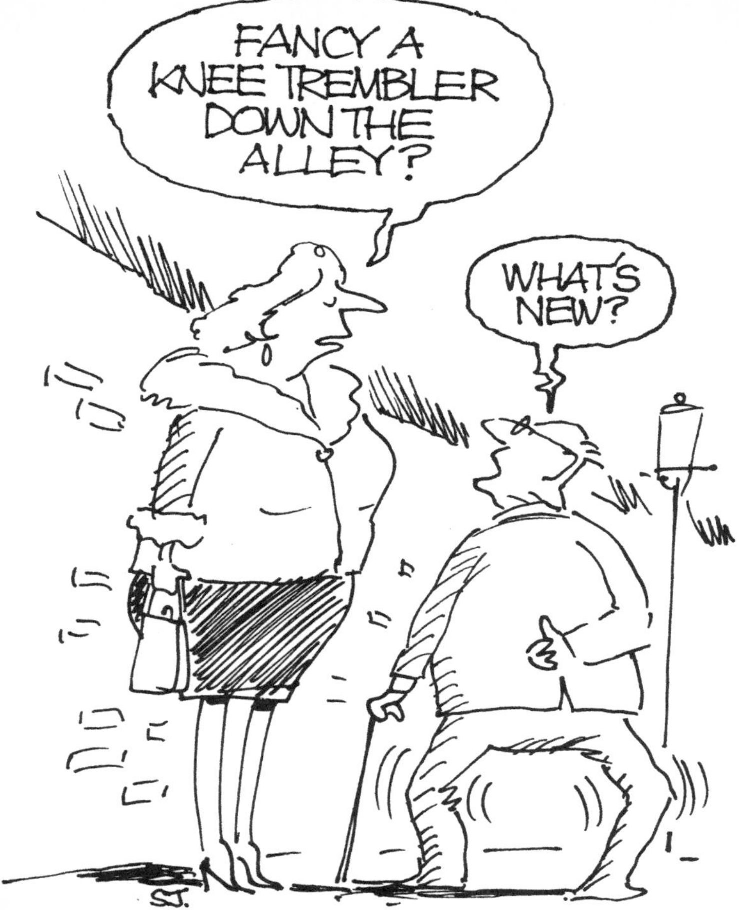
FANCY A KNEE TREMBLER DOWN THE ALLEY?
WHAT'S NEW?
SJ.

DO YOU KNOW WE HAVEN'T MADE LOVE FOR OVER 30 YEARS
34 TO BE PRECISE
S.J.

THIS ISN'T THE GARDEN OF EDEN - GO AND PUT SOME CLOTHES ON THIS MINUTE
ST.

IS IT TRUE YOU'RE PLANNING A SECOND HONEYMOON?
YES... AS SOON AS I CAN FIND A FELLA
TROLLY PARK

HOW CAN YOU SIT AT THAT THING FOR HOURS ON END?
COS I'M ON A COMMODE THAT'S HOW
SJ.

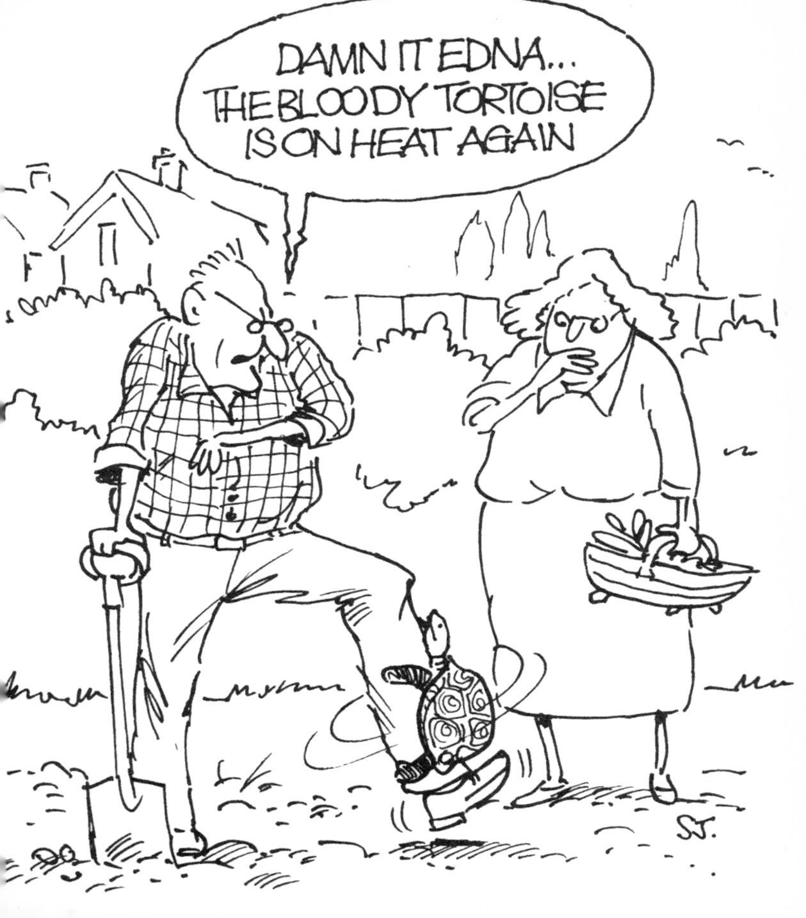
DAMN IT EDNA...
THE BLOODY TORTOISE
IS ON HEAT AGAIN
SJ.